A
HURRICANE
In My
Head

BLOOMSBURY EDUCATION
Bloomsbury Publishing Plc
50 Bedford Square, London, WC1B 3DP, UK

BLOOMSBURY, BLOOMSBURY EDUCATION and the Diana logo are trademarks of Bloomsbury Publishing Plc

First published in Great Britain in 2019 Bloomsbury Publishing Plc
Text copyright © Matt Abbott, 2019 except Remarkable Lives (page 40) © Academies Enterprise Trust.
Used with permission.
Illustrations copyright © Nigel Baines, 2019

Matt Abbott and Nigel Baines have asserted their rights under the Copyright, Designs and Patents Act, 1988,
to be identified as Author and Illustrator of this work

A catalogue record for this book is available from the British Library
ISBN: PB: 978-1-4729-6350-5; ePDF: 978-1-4729-6349-9; ePub: 978-1-4729-6351-2

2 4 6 8 10 9 7 5 3 1

Text design by Amy Cooper

Printed and bound by CPI (UK) Ltd, Croydon, CR0 4YY

To find out more about our authors and books visit www.bloomsbury.com and sign up for our newsletters

A HURRICANE In My Head

POEMS FOR WHEN YOUR PHONE DIES

MATT ABBOTT

Illustrated by Nigel Baines

BLOOMSBURY EDUCATION

LONDON OXFORD NEW YORK NEW DELHI SYDNEY

To my sister, *Rosa*,
for sharing my childhood with me
before either of us had phones.

CONTENTS

Home Life

Growing

The World

The Worlds Inside Our Heads

1.   Keep This a Secret

Before you read this book,
you need to know,
it is a

TOP SECRET

possession.

Reading poetry out of choice
is a dangerous confession.

They'll laugh at you
and ridicule
and say that you're a geek,
even though
(in secret)
it'll help you through the week.

Poetry is magic,
but it must be enjoyed alone.
If you want to read it in public,
then read it on your phone.

If you feel the need to discuss it,
discuss it with yourself.
It won't help your reputation,
but it helps your mental health.

And if you have a trusted friend,
who's down and out of luck...
say:

'KEEP THIS A SECRET!'

and then tell them to read this book.

2. Limerick #1: Cork

There was once a teacher from Cork,
who tried to eat soup with a fork.
It went viral in minutes,
but he decided to bin it,
when they swapped all his chopsticks
for chalk.

SCHOOL LIFE

3. The Snooze Button Blues (Before)

With a duvet as heavy as my heart,
and a bedroom as comfy as a cuddle...

A mattress as soft
as a toasted marshmallow,
and limbs as light
as leaves on a puddle...

This world is so callous and cruel.
Five days a week, imprisoned at school.

My alarm clock was torture
at quarter to eight.

I've stalled it three times,
and now I'm bound to be late!

I just want to roll over,
and starfish
and snooze.

Eyelids half open,
with the snooze button blues.

4. Felt-Tip T-Shirts

T-shirts tucked in schoolbags
for the final day.
That steady summer morning
which seemed so far away...

A countdown which intensified
over those long years,
as we grew with our friends
and overcame our fears.

The assembly
is a summary
from the teachers.

The lesson plans are mainly games
and far from being quiet,
and we know – we just know –
at the final bell, we

RIOT!

There's a symphony of laughter
with a solo from the shrieks;
there are huddled warm embraces,
there are crimson-coloured cheeks;
there are waterfalls of tears
amidst an atmosphere of joy;
butterflies in the bellies
of every girl and every boy.

Fistfuls
of rainbow coloured felt-tip pens.
Messages of love
and autographs from friends.

Like a giant cotton Christmas card,
on a day we'll never forget.
We leave our sports day T-shirt
soaked in ink, instead of sweat.

5.   Pulling a Sickie: An Expert Guide

Academy Awards for acting
are vastly inferior
to successfully pulling
a sickie.

The first time? Easy.
The second? Perhaps.
After that?
It becomes seriously tricky.

So, summon your symptoms,
weaken your voice
and prepare for interrogation.

Beware of how actions
can contrast your words
under **CONSTANT** observation.

You'll have to go hungry
(eat toast at a push)
and move around slowly
(amidst all the rush)
and feign disappointment
(I know this is tough)
and don't sound sarcastic
(you'll call your own bluff!)

Be a stickler for detail;
did it start in the night?
'When you crept off at bedtime,
you did seem all right...'

Play down the importance
of this *particular* day
(they're equally vital,
but that's how you play).

You can't control your temperature,
and you can't control your complexion.
So you'll need some Grade A acting skills
to fake that pesky infection.

It's a tightrope of mischief:
give heartstrings a tug!
'There were loads off yesterday...
it must be a bug...'

Use Google if you need to,
but only a touch.
It's deeply suspicious
if you reel off too much.

Stay true to the cause,
with puppy-dog eyes.
And remember: freedom
is the ultimate prize.

6. Big School

In a sprawling concrete universe,
a labyrinth of corridors,
where everybody knows the way:
all except for me.

Every classroom's in disguise.
Every corner is a mystery.
I got lost after Geography,
and now I'm late for History.

My cheeks resemble beetroots.
My books are heavy as bronze.
I fight for breath whilst older kids
all glide about like swans.

Teachers tap their watches.
They sigh and roll their eyes.
But this school is like a city:
deep and vast as summer skies.

One by one, the other kids
are joining queues and talking.
But I'm completely clueless
as to whereabouts I'm walking.

I know they call it 'Big School',
but these buildings are gigantic.
It's super chilled at break time,
but after bell, its frantic.

And these posters could be hieroglyphs:
they make no sense to me.
These stairs go on forever,
and I'm late for Lesson 3.

I've got my pencil case, my planner,
my lunch box and my books,
but still I'm feeling paranoid
from all the funny looks.

How come they're so popular?
So good at making friends?
I bet they're all just lonely, too.
I bet they just pretend.

I find it hard to swallow,
that everyone knows the way.
It's a maze the size of Mexico
which changes every day.

It's a Rubik's cube
of half-familiar landmarks in my mind.
And why are the scariest teachers
the most difficult to find?

How on earth will I ever get
a single GCSE,
when everybody knows the way:
all except for me...

7. Cast Adrift [Part One]

I remember it like it was yesterday,
but actually, it's been years.
My first week at primary school:
butterflies and tears.

The jumpers were poster red
with the school's name on the chest,
but mine was plain and maroon:
so different from all the rest.

I was cornered in the corridor.
I felt terrified and tiny.
My shoes were scruffy and scuffed;
theirs were new and shiny.

I'd never felt so utterly alone
in all my time on earth.
They'd stripped me of my confidence
and any sense of worth.

Where were the teachers? Where were my friends?
Surely this wasn't allowed?
I was desperate to be rescued,
but drowning in the crowd.

Their laughter was deafening.
I wanted to curl up in a ball.
But then an older kid came and saved me:
so kind and calm and tall.

They sent the bullies walking,
and asked me if I was OK.
And from then, right through 'til summer,
they smiled at me
every day.

8. The Snooze Button Blues (After)

Caught in a crowd! Footpath closed!
Puddles the size of the Atlantic!
Out of breath and out of time:
furious and frantic.

If I'd *just left earlier*,
this morning would be calm.
My monsoon of misfortune
(since snoozing my alarm).

An elephant barges past me
and knocks my bag to the floor.
The collision makes the contents
spread like scandal.

Anxiously, I gather them –
cracked and creased and grubby –
before the world's biggest bus queue
(which I really cannot handle).

And traffic lights just **KNOW**
when you're running late.
The world waits at a crimson bulb:
eager to accelerate.

The bus takes eighteen hours
when it should take eighteen minutes.
Everyone's born with patience,
but I've just reached my limit.

These mornings should be easy.
A smooth and steady cruise.
My monsoon of misfortune
(the snooze button blues).

9.   Homework Excuses

I didn't do my homework because...

- I got lost on my way home and had to hitchhike back
  from Belgium.
- There were some pirates on the river and they looted
  all my books.
- I *did* do it, but the heating broke, and we used it to make a fire.
- I couldn't afford a loaf of bread, and I wanted to feed the ducks.
- My family had a visit from the **QUEEN**.
- I did it on my tablet, and then some lightning struck the screen.
- I spent the night in hospital with a bout of tropical flu.
- My little brother ripped it up and flushed it down the loo.
- I thought you'd set it for *next week*; I wrote it down wrong.
- I swapped my pen for oil paints and it took me far too long.
- I took a detour through the park and it was eaten by a snake.
- I brought it to school this morning and lost it in morning break.
- I left it in the kitchen when I made myself some toast.
- There was a massive gust of wind which blew it off
  towards the coast.

- I did it on my phone, but the rabbit chewed my charger.
- I wrote it under a microscope; I guess I should've done it larger.
- My family took me on an adventure which I didn't know we'd planned.
- We built a castle in the park and I lost it in the sand.
- I did a high five with an alien, and it *ZAPPED* it from my hand...!
- I didn't do my homework, because...

I didn't understand.

10. My Favourite Colour

It was our first ever Art lesson today,
and the teacher told us to paint our names
in our favourite colour.

They taught us how to mix up paints;
to blob, and stir, and fade.
And so off we went, with aprons and brushes,
on a quest for the perfect shade.

Erin says that her favourite colour is 'sparkle'.
Toby says his favourite is the sunlight through the curtains.
Maria's is when rainbows hide in oil on the road.
They ask me what mine is,
and I really can't be certain.

Amy's is when ketchup blends with mayo.
Tyrone's is the colour of his turtle's tongue.
Shruti's is the sunset that she watches through her window.
Billy's is the walk to school, when spring has finally sprung.

I guess mine is my mother's cheeks
when she comes in from the cold.
Or that grass stain, from the greatest summer ever.
In fact, I think it's the brightest flame:
right in the middle of the bonfire.
Or all my classmates' shades of skin
when we stand in line together.

We mixed our colours for fifty minutes
until we got them right.
And then the bell rang,
and we left behind
an avalanche of white.

11. Pulling a Sickie #1

I feel like I've ridden a rollercoaster
after eating a Sunday roast.
I feel like I've climbed up a crow's nest
and then sailed from coast to coast.*

I feel like an anvil has dropped on my head.
The light hurts my eyes
(even though they're not red).
I can *only* survive
if I stay in **THIS BED!**
And the prospect of vomit
has filled me with dread.

I had night sweats and terrors
(they've soaked in my sheets).
I feel a bit dizzy
when I rise to my feet.

My vision is blurry.
Did I mention I'm nauseous?
I would go to school,
but its best to be cautious.

According to rumour,
these symptoms are tropical.
It's all over the school, yeah –
this illness is topical.
No, I'm fine with my Xbox –
there's no need for hospital!
One day off school
is **MISSION
IMPOSSIBLE**...

*This would make you EXTREMELY seasick.

12. I Fell in Love (in Double Maths)

It's time for Double Maths again.
My face is going scarlet.
There's a pupil sitting **parallel**,
between Raheem and Charlotte.

My heart rate began to **multiply**
as soon as we stepped inside.
The **subtraction** of my confidence
is causing this **divide**.

They raise their arm to speak,
and I begin to sweat.
I'm usually good at breathing,
but their voice makes me forget.

These maths exams are hard enough
without the **added** stress,
so imagine how my stomach turned
when they stayed behind for chess!

13. My Teacher Became a Person

Something happened at school today,
which I found odd and weird.
You know that English teacher
with the copper-coloured beard?

He's eight foot tall
and his hair sticks up
and his glasses have liquorice frames.
He wears shirts that look like
grannies' plates –
I'm terrible with names!

Anyway, I was at his desk,
and my homework
was in his hand.
He stroked his beard
and then my book,
and my mouth was dry as sand.

And then, I saw a photograph
which came as a total surprise.
The teacher, with a woman,
and a baby *and* a dog:
I couldn't believe my eyes!

I thought teachers slept in classroom cupboards,
but instead of going to bed,
they sat there cackling in the dark
and wrote lesson plans instead.

They never watch the telly.
They don't have families, or friends.
And whenever you hear a teacher laugh,
you can tell they just pretend.

They don't have lives or interests;
that's why they love detention.
The teachers are trapped here all alone,
and just want a bit of attention.

If he finds out that I spotted it,
it may well make things worsen.
But I'll try that little bit harder,
now that he's become a person...

14. Sports Day Thrills

My fear lies in formulas:
they make me feel sweaty.
I may as well do schoolwork
in Alphabetti Spaghetti.

I mess around and cause mischief.
I'm always getting in trouble.
But if I sit in silence and concentrate,
I end up feeling puzzled.

Sports day is different.
I grasp my chance to shine.
I can feel my lungs inflating
as we stand there in a line.

Speed, skill and agility
all fill my heart with glee.
Because, it's only sports day
when I truly feel free.

15. The Long Walk Home

That person I'm in love with
(the one from **Double Maths**)
ended up stood next to me
in the queue outside the baths.

As we chatted, I was petrified:
my mind kept going blank.
They spoke just like a skateboard,
and I spoke like a tank.

We did have things in common, though,
as fortune cast its spell.
And then we started talking
in the rush at final bell.

They asked me if I was 'walking'
(that's code for walking home).
I knew they lived the opposite way,
but happily I roamed.

We walked and walked across the town
from daffodils to frost.
And whilst I tried to play it cool,
I knew I was desperately lost.

They said, 'All right – see you, then!'
and their smile resembled heaven.
It's just a shame I didn't get home
until twenty-five past seven.

16.   Pulling a Sickie #2

Their cackles in the playground
echo through my dreams.
Their jibes and digs
and jokes
give me shivers.

I know they say it's 'banter'
and 'I need to get a grip,'
but the tears down my cheeks
grow from puddles
to rivers.

I can't face it again
today.
My shoulders tense at the thought.

I don't have the energy
to wear my shield:
my defence has fallen short.

But I'm so embarrassed
about being bullied;
I feel like such a freak,

that I'll have to rely
on my parents' trust
(though it's nearly every week).

I'll pretend that I'm ill;
that my fate is unstoppable.
One day at school
is **MISSION
IMPOSSIBLE**.

17. The School Photo

I either look cross-eyed,
or one eye is closed.
I spent all night at the mirror
perfecting my pose.

My hair is like a scarecrow's;
it's fallen out of place.
The wind's in my fringe
and the sun's in my face.

I'll grin like a toddler,
and then I'll show my mum.
She'll say:
'You're meant to look all grown-up, now –
you stick out like a sore thumb!'

Why is it,
when we all say:

'CHEESE!'

I'm suddenly out of luck?
My collar's gone all wonky
and my shirt's come untucked.

They'll have it on the classroom wall
for all to smirk and snigger.
Every time I mess it up,
they decide to print it bigger.

But before long,
they'll gather dust
in boxes up on shelves.
And one thing I've learnt about photos is,
people only look
at themselves.

18. Remarkable Lives

I'm gonna take you on a treasure hunt.
It starts inside your mind.
The clue is something remarkable,
that only you can find.
'Cause like the spirals in your fingerprints,
you are unique.
So drown out your inner doubts:
allow bravery to speak.

Here's a challenge:
think of someone remarkable.
And not on social media,
but in your everyday life.
From your family,
or your besties,
or your school.
They might be softer than a kitten,
or sharper than a knife.

It might be a cuddle, or a chuckle
that finds the rainbows in the rain.
Gentle generosity,
or a bright and brilliant brain.
The fact is, you know them,
and you can be remarkable too.
When you start to push your limits,
you'll be amazed at what you can do.

Dance with curiosity.
Leap with aspiration.
Gobble down discovery
and run with conversation.

When it feels as though the world is built
to make you feel small,
just remember: it's remarkable
that you're even here at all.

When it comes to defining *your* expectations,
the only person that's truly in charge
is *you*.
Sometimes they're far too high,
but most times, they're far too low.
And deep down, only you know
what you're truly able to do.

Remarkable is kindness.
Remarkable is respect.
Remarkable is considering how your actions have an
    effect.
Remarkable is patience.
Remarkable is pride.
Remarkable is, no matter what happens, knowing that
    you've tried.

So... take yourself on a treasure hunt.
Turn your brain into a carnival.
This is where I challenge you
to find *your* remarkable.

Remarkable lives surround;
there's potential to be found;
they are waiting to be crowned;
so over to you...
spread it around.

19. Sports Day Chills

It's when we're in the changing room
that I really start to fret.
My brow, palms and lower back
are lined with icy sweat.

I like exercise in books and sheets,
but not outside on grass.
Especially when the whole school
is gathered there en masse.

My laces have come undone.
My shorts are falling down.
This is when a bookworm
transforms into a clown.

'Ready,
steady...
GO!'

My heart could nearly burst.
If there were twenty kids in a race,
I'd come twenty-first.

My cheeks are two tomatoes.
I've got tennis balls for knees.
'Sir, I've sprained my ankle –
can I go to the library please?'

Whoops, cheers, whistles, groans:
it drives me 'round the bend.
My favourite part of sports day
is when sports day comes to an end.

20. Cast Adrift [Part Two]

They're so easy to miss
when they're timid or small:
whether football in the field,
or assembly in the hall.
The younger kids vanish
when friendliness leaves;
fear on their faces
and snot on their sleeves.

Except yesterday, we were walking
(my friend and me),
from the bustle of break time
to Period 3,
when we spotted a circle
of cackling hyenas.
We edged slightly closer,
'cause we knew they hadn't seen us.

There was one kid in the middle,
who looked terrified to death.
They were blubbering so much,
they were struggling for breath.
We were close enough now
to listen to the jeers.
I felt nervous, 'cause those kids
are the meanest in the year.

I'm not good at confronting,
or comfy in a crowd,
and my heart's beating faster –
they're nasty and they're loud.
But this poor kid looks petrified.
Shrinking by the second!
And then my friend stepped forward,
calmly, and beckoned.

'Don't listen to them', they said.
'They're selfish, mean and vile.
We'll walk you to class
and meet you at lunch –
you can hang out with us for a while.'
The bullies protested,
but my friend stood firm, and said,
'You lot should all be ashamed.'
The silence that followed
let the small kid break free,
and brought an end to this pitiless game.

I'm so proud of my friend.
I hope the bullies saw sense.
You should never have fun
at others' expense.

21.   Haiku #1: Assembly

Cheeks turn to lava,
standing up in assembly:
a spotlight of shame.

22. The Careers Advisor

Today I went into an office
(really it was just a small classroom which had been converted),
and in that office,
somebody was supposed to tell me
what career I'm supposed to take.
But in order to do that,
I had to first tell them what kind of career I'd like to take.
It went like this:

CAREERS ADVISOR: What kind of career would you like to take?
ME: I'd like to be a poet, please.
CA: A poet? As a career?
ME: Yes.
CA: Oh. I see. Well, do you not think you could try something more...
important?
ME: I think a poet does a very important job.
CA: And what exactly makes you think that...?

I took a deep intake of breath.

ME: You get poems at weddings, and poems at funerals. Poems can make you laugh, cry, gasp, reminisce, escape, discover, wonder, realise and resolve. They can make you relax and they can fire you up. They can help you unwind and they can motivate you. Poems say the things that normal people can't put into words – sometimes about people that the poet hasn't even met. And sometimes poems say things that people wouldn't be able to say in a normal conversation. Some poems last for hundreds of years, and some poems say more about the world right now than any of the news channels or politics people. So, in a way, really, a poet has an **INCREDIBLY** important career.

There was an awkward pause from the perplexed Careers Advisor, who then said:

'Hmm.
How about Digital Marketing?'

23. Limerick #2: Brighton

There was once a teacher from Brighton,
who was very difficult to frighten,
until one day in town
they bumped into a clown,
and in *seconds*,
their cheeks, they had whitened.

HOME LIFE

24. My Family's Gone Camping

The mallet may have bent the pegs
and bashed my dad's thumb,
but the guy ropes are all in place
(from the expertise of Mum).

There's a porch, and a pointy roof,
and a section on either side,
and zips and clips and pockets
(where the creepy-crawlies hide).

I've got a sleeping bag, and a roll-out mattress,
and a torch I can strap to my head.
I'm gonna creep out and gaze at constellations
when my parents have gone to bed.

We're gonna wake up on top of sheets
that are moist and made of grass;
instead of smooth, dry cotton
(from the beds of days gone past).

We'll dream amongst the animals:
the badgers and the foxes.
Every item is in a bag
(instead of shelves and boxes).

There's a toy soldier's drum roll
whenever it starts to rain.
Mum wakes up grumpy
(Dad's been snoring like a train).

Brekkie comes in tins and pouches
(made in pots and pans).
This is how our family lived
in the days of tribes and clans.

It was troublesome in summer,
and in autumn it began to harden.
I just really hope by winter,
we won't be camping in the garden!

25. The Supermarket Blues

There's nothing more likely
to make you sigh and flop,
than compulsory attendance
at a supermarket shop.

The aisles are like motorways,
and only seem to grow, except,
everyone in the supermarket
is excruciatingly

What's the point in reading labels?!
Just stick it in the trolley!
I'd rather wait outside,
even though it's raining,
and I don't have a brolly.

Round and round the supermarket,
like a snail doing Formula One.
Toilet paper, bleach and coffee.
We walk past anything fun.

And just when I think it's finished;
I've escaped the supermarket blues,
we crawl towards the checkouts,
and I see the size of the queues!

26. Sock Loyalty

There's a hole in my sock,
and its growing.
In the winter,
my big toe is cold.

But this *specific* pair
are my comfiest
(even though
they're outrageously old).

They're rainbow-coloured
with patterns and stripes
(or they *might* just be
plain black).

And I'll always be loyal
to my favourite pair
(until I'm given
a brand-new pack).

27. Verb Alarm

When Dad says he's gonna 'jump' in the shower,
I hope he doesn't *actually* jump (he might slip).
And when Mum says she's 'running' to the loo,
I've never seen her *actually* run.

How do you 'nip' to the shops?
Do you have to pinch somebody's arm?
And can you only 'dash' to the car?
These verbs are causing alarm...

We 'slope off' to bed
and 'wander into' town.
We 'trek' to the supermarket
(usually with a frown),
and we 'stop' for a coffee
(but never dessert),
and if you 'fall' out of love,
I guess that's why it hurts...

28. My Favourite Friend

They sing at the bus stop
and dance in the rain.
Their laughter's a blanket
that cuddles my brain.

On concrete-coloured mornings,
they always bring a spark.
The kind of personality
that could glow in the dark.

They do impressions of teachers
that leave me in stitches.
They sort out my mindset
when it wakes up with glitches.

They sooth and excite me;
move and delight me;
improve and ignite me;
and all the rest.

They're loyal and funny
and clever and brave.
I've got plenty of friends,
but they are the

BEST.

29. Birthday Invitations

Mum says I can invite **ANYONE**,
up to a maximum of twenty.
I said that I wanted a **THOUSAND** more,
but she insists that it's plenty.

It's an enormous opportunity
that simply can't be missed,
so I cleared my throat and said, 'All right, Mum:
here's my birthday list...'

- Prince Harry & Meghan Markle (I'll write it in
    sparkly pen).
- Cousins Joe & Amelia (they can help me build a den).
- Ed Sheeran can sing a song when they bring along
    my candles.
- Granddad can come (but he mustn't wear socks
    and sandals).
- I want Elsa from *Frozen* (supposing that she's free).
- I want every single mermaid that lives out at sea.
- I want Messi and Ronaldo and both of their teams.
- I want to meet the people that make the funniest
    memes.

- I want a selection of the animals from the biggest carousel.
- Emmeline Pankhurst and Shakespeare as well.
- I want Amelia to bring Sophie, and Joe to bring Jamaal.
- I want Julia Donaldson, J.K. Rowling, oh – and Roald Dahl!
- I want every Queen there's ever been,
- and every King that brought the ring,
- and instead of a cake, a chocolate fountain.

Hold on, Mum - have you been counting?!

30. Family Holiday

I thought holidays were exciting,
and something to embrace,
but Mum keeps hissing angrily,
and Dad's got a very red face.

And it's FAR too early in the morning:
even earlier than school!
I hope this place has a water slide,
and a jacuzzi, and a pool.

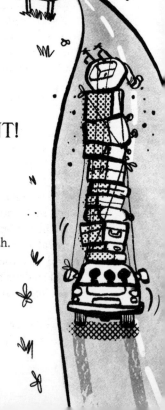

The boot of the car is bursting.
We've half of the house on the roof.
They tell me it's only a little drive,
but I don't think that's the truth.

And I know we have a sat nav,
but Dad's brought a map.
The window is my pillow
so I'm struggling to nap.

And what's this on the radio?!
These songs are truly ANCIENT!
I want to stop and run around,
but they say I need to be patient.

This motorway we're driving on
is the longest road on earth!
Its only eight in the morning,
but it's like I've been here since birth.

My tablet's in the suitcase.
My hope has disappeared.
We drive, and drive, and drive, and drive,
and still we're nowhere near.

I study the massive map.
The roads all look like veins.
But how do we know where the car is?
And why aren't they as fast as trains?

We've been driving
for *two whole hours* now,
are we in the USA?
It still just looks like Britain:
all boring and cloudy and grey.

But then Mum and Dad
start singing songs
and tell little stories,
and pass me a sweet that tastes
like knickerbocker glory.

And we take it in turns to name animals
and make noises from the zoo.
We play 'I Spy' until emerald fields
reveal a stretch of blue.
And then the laughter stops,
and so does the car,
but imaginations run...

We take a gulp of ocean air
and the holiday's begun...

31. Haiku #2: Party Poopers

Why do my parents
pluck me from parties *before*
we've had the ice cream?!

32. The Family Wedding Blues

On a day that lasts an eternity,
and sees all the fun get fired,
why – when we enter the evening –
are the parents not **WOEFULLY** tired?!

They must have chores in the morning?
Must be *desperate* to leave by now?
Its quarter to nine, and I'm yawning.
What's the point – they've made all the vows...?

Dad's got his tie 'round his forehead.
He's sliding about on his knees.
They're singing along to **EXTREMELY** old songs.
I'm exhausted from issuing pleas.

Mum is **OUTRAGEOUSLY** thirsty.
She keeps on refilling her glass.
Either that, or it's delightfully tasty:
half caffeine,
and half laughing gas.

And I know that their dancing is awful,
but some people have started to cry...
Cousins and grandmas, uncles and aunts,
with no sign of waving goodbye.

I watch them falling about,
all tailored and made-up and frilly.
Why do they *insist* on dressing so smart,
before acting so silly?!

33. Sheila

Even when you're ill,
there's still a little thrill
when you're too ill
to go to school.
But I arrived home today
to find my mum (not at work),
with a face that showed how life
can be cruel.

'Sit down, my darling,'
she ushered.
I'd never heard her voice
so weak.
Candyfloss soft,
with a sorrowful tone.
She had mascara
down her cheek.

Mums aren't supposed
to look like this.
She looked tired, and empty,
and broken.
I sat down,
and she pulled me in for a kiss.
And then I braced myself,
for the words about to be spoken.

'Last night,
your nan went to sleep.
But this morning
when they checked on her in bed,
she'd slipped away peacefully
in her pastel pink nightie.
I'm really sorry, sweetheart
– but she's dead.'

She loved to eat these
toffee-flavoured sweets,
and have her television
deafeningly high.
She loved fridge magnets, Radio 2,
Coronation Street and bingo,
and I'll never get the chance
to say, 'goodbye.'

I hugged my mum for ages
and cried into her chest.
My world went
from a loaf of bread to crumbs.
I don't know how to deal with death,
but I'll try my best to be brave.
After all – my mum's
lost her mum.

34. Ball Games

It's a fear reserved for Voldemort
or a Tyrannosaurus Rex;
a dread that leaves you frozen
to the spot.

It should be plain and simple
but it's painfully complex:
and just to avoid the question,
we will plan and scheme and plot.

We've been playing *extremely* carefully;
gentle and precise.
And it wouldn't be as dreadful
if we'd only done it twice,

but we're well beyond the limit now:
over half-a-dozen.
The neighbours see two criminals,
but it's only me and my cousin.

Fences, gates, walls and drives,
the fortress holds our golden prize.
If all else fails,
we're on our knees:

'Excuse me, mister…
can we have our ball back, please?'

GROWING

35. Outside the Cinema #1

They insisted that I'm too young
to be going on a date.
That I don't understand what it means,
and I should stick with my friends
and wait.
I'm not 'emotionally mature enough'
to form this kind of bond.
But what's the point in having feelings,
if you're not allowed to respond...?

I'm stood outside the cinema
with **20** minutes to spare.
I watched **19** tutorials
to fine-tune my hair.
The '**18**' films look wicked,
but none of them we'll see.
My cousin's **17**,
and still needs I.D.

16 minutes spare.
My heart beats like a drum.
15 pounds in my pocket
(a reluctant gift from Mum).
'**14** was the minimum age
I even *considered* kissing.'
13 hours later,
she was still reminiscing.

The '**12**' films look decent.
I reckon we'll be fine.
I wonder what we'll talk about
when we're standing there in line?

It takes **11** footballers
to make a stadium roar,
but you sent a single message,
and my jaw was on the floor.
When you said you'd come and meet me,
I felt **10** feet tall.
9 o'clock it finishes:
my mum says I've got to call.
I said, 'Mum – that'd be embarrassing.
You're acting like I'm **8**!'
7 minutes spare
and my nerves are in a **STATE**!

6 minutes spare.
My lungs are trying to skive!
I try to count steadily,
but get distracted after **5**.

4 eyes set to meet:
I don't believe it's true.
If a genie gave me wishes,
all **3** of them would be you.

2 souls, that are songs
just waiting to be sung.
1 night to prove, undoubtedly,
that I am **NOT TOO YOUNG**.

36. My Adult Diet Riot

Imagine being old enough
to buy your *own* shopping,
and be in charge
of what you eat
and **WHEN.**

I'd have Sunday roast for breakfast,
cheese on toast for dinner,
and then a chocolate banana sundae
at half-past ten.*
For lunch?

I'd have Pick 'n' Mix,
and sushi and tapas for snacks.
Pizza instead of porridge,
and **ENTIRE** multipacks.

My adult diet riot
(which my childhood severely lacks).

*at **NIGHT**!

37. My Younger Brother's Dribble

My age is double digits.
I'm wonderfully mature.
But my younger brother fidgets
and dribbles on the floor.

I try my best to remember
when I was so unrefined,
but it's all a little hazy:
my brother's only nine.

38. Outside the Cinema #2

There's a hurricane in my head,
and woodpeckers in my fingers.
I try and think of something else,
but still the feeling lingers.

My stomach's doing somersaults
and my eyes are darting about.
I feel too weak to whisper,
but deep down, I need to shout.

Maybe your bus was late,
or maybe it's because,
when I said it felt too good to be true,
it turns out, it actually was...

39. Twelve Years Young

I don't want to be a teenager.
I've heard they're stinky and smelly.
They get spots that grow on cheeks and chins;
round and red like jelly.

They're always starting arguments
and slamming bedroom doors.
They do start getting pocket money,
but they have to do the chores...

Growth spurts and hormones
and mood swings and HAIR.
Whenever I hear about teenagers,
it gives me a massive scare.

I'm not ready to be a teenager.
Twelve's enough for me!
So here's to staying forever young,
and bright, and fun,
and

free.

40. Limerick #3: Chester

There was once a teacher from Chester
whose pupils had never impressed her,
until the last day of term –
she smiled with a squirm –
when Jacob came dressed as a jester.

41. The Spine-Tingling Horror of 0%

OH NO! MY PHONE HAS DIED...

No power, no socket,
no charger or cable.
Just a sad-looking phone
lying blank on the table.

No voltage,
and no more vibrations.
No more emojis,
no notifications.

I've tried it and tried it,
but the battery is flat.
It might work for ten seconds,
but it's gone after that.

If I could *just* share that photo
or finish that text,
I'm certain my mind
wouldn't be quite as vexed.

I charged it for hours:
all green in its glory.
But I just can't resist
all those video stories.

So, I try to forget it,
and I go meet my friends.
No need to show off
and no need to pretend.

I don't know how I'll manage,
but I'll give it a shot.
Unbridled imagination
is the only thing I've got...

42. Push

I shouldn't have to lie about my age.
You can't say I'm not old enough
for a webpage.
My online persona,
these profiles that I craft;
those filters and emojis,
the times that we laughed.

I choose who I follow:
who I talk to.
And even though we've never met,
we effortlessly gel.
And one day, I'll look like that,
and have as many things.
My world will be as likeable,
with all the joy that brings.

My mother tried to ban me,
but she gave in later.
I'm a shadow in the playground,
but a superstar on data, and –

– a push notification. Abuse from a stranger.
An insult leaves my inbox full of dirt.
The feeling in my stomach, does not consist of pixels;
I can put my phone in flight mode, but the words still hurt.

It's not like a push
in the playground.
The only person who saw it
was me.
And now I feel scared
as I swipe with my thumb.
There might be things
I don't feel
old enough
to see.

43. Nature's Prank

This is a DISASTER.
The heaviest of blows.

I have the TV remote all to myself,
and I want my favourite shows.

But I can't see a single pixel.
Nature's played a prank!

The sunlight's left my flat screen
looking blank.

I've tried to close the curtains,
but they're just too heavy and tall.

I've sat at every single angle,
but the sunshine's covering the wall.

It's like I'm living in a marathon,
but I can only crawl.

I shrug my shoulders and switch it off.
I'll just have to play with my ball...

44. The Good Old Days

I remember, before I had a phone,
life was so much richer.

Instead of waiting anxiously
for comments on my picture,

I would hunt for creepy-crawlies,*
or make up dance routines,**

and chat to friends in real life
(instead of on a screen).

* recommended for girls
** recommended for boys

45. Outside the Cinema #3

My dad said he'd treat me to the cinema,
because he knew I'd had a terrifying test.
He said, 'No matter what the result is,
we know you've tried your best.'

I told him about all my revision techniques,
and then a memory surrounded by bricks.
He put his hand on my shoulder and asked:
'How about Pick 'n' Mix?'

But as we approached the entrance,
my shoes stuck to the spot.
Some nasty kids from the year above
were cooking up a plot.

'Ooh look – it's Simon!' they yelled.
He said, 'How do they know my name...?'
My dad looked down with stern concern,
and I felt full of shame.

'Why don't you paint us a picture, DAD?!'
I started to panic and fret.
He asked me, 'Where are they getting this from?!'
I was riddled with regret.

He looked sad, and weak, and unsettled.
Not strong, and calm, and brave.
And now I just feel mortified,
because I've tried so hard to behave.

I share my life on social media.
I give it away for free.
And unless you make it private,
it's there
for all to see...

46. The Posh Hotel

'It's a treat!' Mum says.
We're in Abergavenny,
in a hotel that cost her a million pennies.

'It's *four* stars!' she declares,
as she passes us our bags,
and we walk to the entrance (all regal, with flags).

The keys
are a *wooden* spinning top,
instead of a plastic card.

Chandeliers,
and paintings
of men that look like guards.

Spiral staircase,
fluffy robes
and biscuits by the drinks.

I can't wait to stick it
on my profile,
and see what my classmates think.

This hotel is SICK!
I'm gonna spend the whole time
pretending we've won the lottery.

Parents excited
by the dullest things
(like the shower and the pottery).

I *thought* this place was perfect:
the finest hotel
you've EVER seen,

but we went down for breakfast
in the morning, and there were

NO BAKED BEANS!

47. Rules for Boys and Rules for Girls

BOYS

If you're feeling sad and overwhelmed,
cry **EXACTLY** like a girl.
Bring emotions to the surface,
or climb on your bed and curl.

Articulate your feelings:
expression equals strength.
If anyone says otherwise,
keep them at arm's length.

Be open and be honest.
Have faith in what you believe.
Be true to who you are.
Wear your heart upon your sleeve.

GIRLS

If your hands need to be dirty,
so be it.
Don't be shamed for being sweaty
when you're trying to keep fit.

If playing sport excites you,
then play until you're shattered.
Show snide remarks a pair of heels:
they simply do not matter.

Be it science or technology,
or a hammer with a nail:
if that's what floats your boat... just smile
and let it sail.

48. Outside the Cinema #4

I don't know what this film's about,
but I'm giving it a shot.
I'm a little bored of special effects,
so I hope it has a plot.

Explosions and aliens
and princesses dressed in pink:
very pleasing on the eye,
but I like films that make me think.

I want to go home quoting dialogue.
I want the twists and turns.
I want a special buzz from the characters
which constantly returns.

I want strength in women,
and weakness in men,
and for the pocket money I'm spending,
I hope they don't just wrap it up
with another
happy ending.

49. Football is NOT for Girls

There's something about boys and football
that leaves me feeling curious.
Why do they love it so much,
when it leaves them feeling furious?

My dad and my brother get
SO ANNOYED
when it doesn't go their way.
Why do they follow their football team,
when they hate to watch them play?

I always try and join them
when they watch it on the telly,
but my brother yells,
'IT'S NOT FOR GIRLS!'
and I feel a rage in my belly.

They get angry whenever they watch it;
I get angry when I'm not allowed.
And how come the cameras show us
pretty women in the crowd?

I don't understand why they can watch,
even though it's not for girls...?
Some of us love to slide in mud:
it's not all curtseys and twirls.

But then something happened
that summer,
when the world went football-mad.
My eyes lit up like floodlights:
it silenced my brother and dad.

Female commentators, female pundits,
and in the studios, female pros.
PROFESSIONALS,
who played for their **COUNTRY**.
I swear, I nearly froze.

Football *is* for girls.
The boys are just being greedy.
I watched some women online:
we're skilful and we're speedy.

I feel excited and inspired,
and I know I'm not alone.
If there's one thing
I've learnt about life,
it's that there's more
than what we're shown.

50. Haiku #3: Valentine's Card

A Valentine's card,
painfully anonymous,
to my same-sex friend.

51.   Man Up

People are fragile,
regardless of their gender.
If emotions are getting the better of you,
it's vital to surrender.

And if boys show
their sensitive side,
and they're ridiculed
or mocked,

their emotions are being buried
and their confidence is knocked.

It's a lethal combination
which worsens over the years.
So, don't ever tell them to 'man up,'
because it'll only end

in tears.

52. Limerick #4: Stoke

There was once a teacher from Ossett
(you've never heard of Ossett, have you?
Never mind...)

There was once a teacher from Stoke,
who knew the world's funniest joke.
His lessons were dour
for nearly an hour
and then you'd laugh so much
you could choke.

THE
WORLD

53. Haiku #4: Clocks Fall Back

There's no sweeter sleep
than when the time slips backwards:
stolen golden hour.

54. The Secret Door

Whenever I take a detour
to walk to school with my friends,
we pass this old and secret door
(where Station Road bends).

It's weary-looking: cobweb-coated,
in need of a lick of paint.
Soil brown, with sand-coloured writing
(peeling off, and faint).

'NO ENTRY!'

it says,
with a rusty padlock
(chunky, and tilting to the right).

And I've always wondered,
'What's in there?!'
when I've lain in bed
at night.

It could be a secret tunnel,
with skeletons and treasure and **TRAPS**.
It could be a tiny cupboard,
where all the spiders nap.

It might be full of equipment
and machinery and tools.
It might be a special meeting place
where adults invent the rules.

There could be a ladder underground
or a helicopter pad.
It could be the Ministry of Merry
or the Society of Sad.

There might be a swimming pool, a science lab,
a recording studio or a gym.
Joe Ellis says he broke inside,
so I guess I could just ask him...

55. The Ice Cream Van

He's never liked football.
In fact, he despises it.
But when he hears that jingle
– *Match of the Day* –
his brain's replaced by popping candy.

Eyeballs must seek approval.
Eager and wide;
there's no time for words.
A fistful of silver
and a heart full of joy.
He bounds for the pavement
and then, towards ice cream.

The menu could never do justice
to the tingles and textures and tastes.
And the ice cream woman is weary,
but she lives for that look on his face.

He counts up his coins,
and squints at the prices,
and then leaps to a final decision.
Screwballs and sauces and lollies and licks:
he'll glide down that pavement
whatever he picks.

56. Haiku #5: Clocks Spring Forwards

When time springs forwards,
alarm clocks are agony,
and rage begs to dream.

57. My Favourite Sounds

The jingle of keys in my mum's hand
when she's walking down the path:
arriving home
from a long day at work.

That little bit of silence
in between the laughter,
when you know the laughter
hasn't stopped
as you hold a pregnant pause.

A special trip to the swimming pool
for an afternoon of fun:
echoed splashes blending
with the shouts and the whistles.

Birdsong on a Sunday morning.
The world takes a breath.

The gentle squeak of the gates
in the playground at the park.

The screams and squeals and cheers
in the school yard at lunchtime.

The rollercoaster slowing down
when you're right at the front of the queue.

The crackle of the bonfire,
and the shrills and thrills of the fireworks.

The pan in the kitchen bubbling
with all your favourite flavours.

A playlist on shuffle,
and it drops your favourite tune.

When your best friend does that silly voice
that no one else has heard.

When your shoes crunch
in untouched snow
on a crisp winter morning.

When the rain batters on the window
but you're snuggled up inside.

When the waves lap on the shore,
and the seagulls sing above.

The whisper of a loved one
that makes you feel safe.

The chorus of 'Happy Birthday'
when all eyes fix on you.
Someone saying, 'I love you,'
and you knowing that it's true.

58. Maria

Maria's tears
must be massive,
because she has beautiful
big brown eyes.

She has more freckles on her forehead
(and her nose and her cheeks)
than stars
in the starriest of skies.

Whenever she tells a story,
the whole world pauses:
every sentence that she speaks
is a prize.

And Maria once told me
she likes to pretend
that she's a panda
in disguise.

Why do we dream of fame and fortune?
It'll only end in defeat.
And there's nothing quite as precious in life
as the people that you meet.

59. My Favourite Place

Clouds shaped like camels
made of cotton wool,
swimming through a
rooftop pool.

Leaves the shade of lizards
do a ballerina's twirl,
as the wind in the trees
makes the sound of the ocean.

The grass looks like whiskers
on my History teacher's face,
and this park on a Friday
is my very favourite place.

60. Silent Disguise

I can't afford a phone that plays music,
but I found a pair of earphones,
so I wear them to pretend.

I take one out when someone tries to talk to me,
and they help me feel invisible
when I can't find a friend.

61. Outside the Cinema #5

Don't bore me with too much storyline.
I want blood! Gore! Action!
I'm not listening to the radio;
I want visual satisfaction.

I want fireballs and helicopters,
dinosaurs as well.
Motorbikes in outer space
or a poltergeist hotel.

I want spiders with **SIX** heads
and aeroplanes under the sea.
Entire cities up in flames
and tigers as tall as trees.

Transport me to another dimension.
Create a universe on the screen.
Show me things in pixels
that no human has ever seen.

Blockbusters, bigger than ever!
Widescreen and wild.
Don't make cinema boring
if you're making it
for a child.

62. Those Who Sleep Outside

Why do people sleep outside
in tents and in doorways,
when there's loads of empty houses
going spare?

Why are people
blatantly ignored
if they're wearing scruffy clothes
and they haven't washed their hair?

We leave change in the tip jar
whenever we buy a coffee,
but we won't stop
to drop it in a cup.

I wish someone
would buy *them* a coffee,
and take the time to ask them,

'What's up?'

63. Limerick #5: Fife

There was once a teacher from Fife
who tried to eat soup with a knife.
He coughed and wheezed
and spluttered and sneezed,
and the soup ended up on his wife.

THE WORLDS INSIDE OUR HEADS

64. Our Washing Machine's Astronaut

I'm fairly sure
that our washing machine
is a spaceship.

The way it **rumbles**
and **SPINS**
and **shakes**.

Sometimes it seems like
our kitchen's
a launch pad:

all the glasses and the plates
and the coffee mugs
would break.

I imagine the tiny astronauts,
getting dizzy
amongst the bubbles.

In a galaxy
with socks
instead of stars.

We feed them all
with powder
before their mission.

I just hope
there's something tastier
on Mars.

What if
some aliens
climbed aboard their spaceship,

and joined us
in the kitchen
for our dinner?

I sit and stare
for hours,
and there's no sign of life...

but I guess,
when it comes to outer space,
I'm only a beginner.

65. Rainbow Milkshake Madness

There's this milkshake, right,
and it's *crazy*.
I'm so excited, I'm struggling to breathe.
It's the colour of a rainbow, man –
you really wouldn't believe!

I've heard these loopy rumours,
and now I finally have the truth.
So sit down and listen:
it'll make you hit the roof!

It costs a hundred billion pounds
from the Apple shop in town.
I carried in my piggy bank
and I tipped it upside down.

It turns out, I could afford it,
so I bought one and grabbed a straw.
I took a drink, and mate,
it was like **NOTHING** I'd tasted before!

At first it tasted like a Big Mac,
so I slurped it in a hurry.
And then yam, and then carrot,
and then... a chicken curry!

And the next bit is insane –
I swear this isn't a lie.

By the time I'd reached the bottom,
the milkshake made me fly!

Yes, that's right:

FLY.

So, I took to the sky,
and I crossed the Atlantic,
and to Disneyland Florida I went.
Lads, I'm telling you now;
it was the best hundred billion
I've ever spent.

Steve Jobs was there – he's alive again –
so I shook his hand with a grin.
And just when it couldn't get better,
Beyoncé back-flipped in.

It was the

BEST THING EVER,

but the reason you've never heard,
is because apparently,
if you drink too much,
it stops you from saying a word.

So, have a bit,
enjoy it,
and then pass it on to your friend.
The Rainbow Milkshake Madness,
where the fun
will never end.

66. Reminder

Do you ever get that thing,
when you're drifting off to sleep,
and then wake with a jolt,
and it feels like you've fallen
into your bed?

Apparently, it's when your body
falls asleep before your brain,
so your brain sends a reminder
that you'd be nothing
without your head.

67. The Best View on Bonfire Night

Seema says, stick a camera on a bee.
Ben says you've to climb to the top
of the tallest hill in town.
Evelyn says, you should climb the tallest tree.
Ibrahim says, be an astronaut:
up above, and looking down...

Imagine ALL the fireworks
through a window up in space.
Like a kaleidoscope exploding,
with urgency and grace.

Like giant neon jellyfish,
or electrified glitter.
Like the sky's sucked a lemon
(only sweet instead of bitter).

Mix popping candy, fairy lights
and the world's fastest car.

Find a bouncy ball bearing
and throw it around a jar.

Burst a hundred million bubble wraps
and you'll still not raise the bar.

The best view on bonfire night
is sat amongst the stars.

68. Our Washing Machine's Alien

Remember when I told you
about our washing machine?
The porthole from our kitchen
to outer space?

Well, it turns out,
I was right all along:
the alien arrived on Tuesday
(with some clothing in a case).

The alien
spoke backwards.
It said, **'OLLEH'**
instead of **'HELLO!'**.

It had iPhones
instead of eyebrows
which its eyeballs
were below.

It's a good job
we were having chilli
so there was enough
to go around.
I laughed so much
I nearly fell off my chair
whenever it made
a sound.

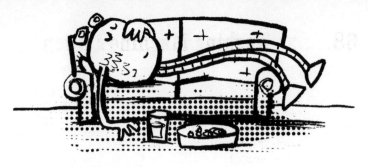

Its skin looked like
the Northern Lights:
lime green, magenta
and blue.

Its voice was like
a synthesiser,
and when it spoke,
its belly button grew.

I wanted to stroke it,
and keep it as a pet,
but if my alien grew ill...
what would I say to the vet?!

It slurped down its chilli,
we nicknamed it Billy,
and we gasped
as it started to glow.

'Farewell, my friends:
I'd better head home.
I've an awfully long way
to go...'*

*'...OG OT
YAW GNOL YLLUFWA NA EV I
EMOH DAEH RETTEB D'I
:SDNEIRF YM ,LLEWERAF'

69. Train Riddle

Silent and white,
and slow and soft,
and **EXTREMELY** expensive
(per journey).
And unless something goes
disastrously wrong,
they're much more One-Way
than Return-y.

Answer: It's the train on a wedding dress!

70. A Message from Matt

Dear poet
(you are a poet;
you just might not know it...
yet).

At the time of writing this,
I'm 29 years old
(I know: nearly 30.
That's ancient).

When I was your age,
all those years ago,
I didn't like poetry
at all.

I didn't like poetry in primary school,
or secondary school,
and I didn't study English
for my A Levels.

I didn't go to university,
and I don't have a certificate
or any qualifications
for poetry.

Whenever we were taught poetry,
it didn't appeal to me;
it didn't *speak* to me,
or say anything about my life.

I did, however, love lyrics.
I loved wordplay and stories.
I loved creating things with language
and I loved to challenge rules.

It just took me a long time
to realise
that poetry
is the artform for me.

Don't be scared by poetry.
Don't worry if you don't understand it.
Don't be put off if you read some poetry
which is utterly dreadful and boring.

As a professional poet,
I try to read new poetry every week,
and I still find *some* poetry
dreadful and boring.

Embrace the enjoyment.
Embrace the anarchy.
Embrace the empowerment.
Embrace the possibilities.

Poetry changed my life forever,
and it can change yours too.
I really hope
that you enjoyed this book:

a **secret**
between
me
and you.

GET WRITING!

RULES FOR WRITING POETRY

Well, the best thing about poetry is, there are no rules. Except for the rules that you choose to follow. And even then, if you don't stick to those rules, you won't get told off. You might get silently sneered at by people who can only stick to rules, but then who cares what they think anyway?

OK, I lied. In my opinion, there is one **golden** rule. Shall I tell you what it is...?

Go on, then...

That rule is **SHOW,** don't *tell*.

Poems can be brilliant for telling stories, but if they sound a bit like a newspaper article or a police report (i.e. they did this and then they went there and then they saw that, etc.) then there's really no point in calling it poetry.

A VERY IMPORTANT SECRET
ABOUT POETRY

Let me tell you a secret. Poetry is a super-power.
Do you know why?

Poetry is when you paint pictures
by putting music into words.

Poetry is when you can take a feeling from your head,
and make it appear in a complete stranger's.

Poetry is when you describe normal things
in a way that nobody else has ever done.

Poetry is all about creating a moment.
And most of all, it's about having fun.

LET'S GO SWIMMING

Here's a challenge for you. You've been to the swimming baths, right? Most people have. If you haven't, then I strongly advise that you do so, and if you can't, then don't worry – it's overrated. Anyway...

I want you to describe the swimming baths using only the **senses.** Most people are lucky enough to have all five, but just use whichever you choose.
I want you to describe it, without ever telling us where you are, but in a way that means we could easily guess. Does that make sense?

If you're stuck for ideas, try and make it contrast with something. For example:

What would you **smell** at the swimming baths, compared to the cinema?
What would you **hear** at the swimming baths, compared to the park?
What do you **feel** at the swimming baths, compared to your bedroom?
What might you **taste** (either before or after, preferably not during),
and what **specifically** would you see...?

Try it for a challenge and then test it on somebody to see how quickly they guess.

If you can do that, then you're a poet...

ACKNOWLEDGEMENTS

Firstly, I'd like to thank Ruth Saxton for inviting me to be one of the 25th birthday ambassadors for Eureka! The National Children's Museum. I used to visit Eureka! as a boy and it was a huge honour to be appointed as a #Eureka25 ambassador. And it was my poem for their birthday which first caught the attention of Bloomsbury Publishing.

Secondly, I'd like to thank Deniece Wheeler from Bloomsbury for making the initial contact, and then Hannah Rolls for commissioning and editing this collection. It's another massive honour for me to be working with a publisher like Bloomsbury and I can't wait to hold this book in my hands.

Thirdly, I'd like to thank every teacher, museum/gallery worker, arts professional and charity worker that's employed me to work with children. I've delivered workshops of all shapes and sizes to a wide range of groups and ages around the UK since 2013, and it's undoubtedly the highlight of my career. I know it sounds cheesy, but I learn just as much from the kids as they do from me, if not more.

My work at The Hepworth Wakefield and the National Coal Mining Museum for England were particularly transformative, and more recently through Academies Enterprise Trust after they commissioned my 'Remarkable Lives' poem.

Finally, I'd like to thank my fiancée, Maria, for supporting me whilst I was writing this book. I took myself down to Plashet Park all summer and sat against a tree writing these poems for hours and hours on end, and Maria was a constant source of encouragement, inspiration and support whenever I came home suffering from writer's anxiety. I'd be nowt without thee.

So, I hope that you enjoy reading these poems, no matter what age you are – at least until your phone has some battery. Cheers.

ABOUT THE AUTHOR

Matt Abbott is a poet, educator and activist from Wakefield, West Yorkshire. He began writing poetry at the age of 17 whilst studying at Ossett Sixth Form and has since gone on to forge a career involving a major label record deal, several national theatre tours and a highly acclaimed one-man show, *Two Little Ducks*.

His style is vernacular and accessible, and his main drive is to ignite a love for poetry in people of all ages – particularly those who consider it a dull and irrelevant artform. He is an ambassador for Eureka! The National Children's Museum and lead creative writing practitioner at The Hepworth Wakefield.

His début adult collection *Two Little Ducks (And Selected Poems 2015–2018)* was published in October 2018. *A Hurricane In My Head* is his first collection for children. He teaches workshops in a wide range of environments around the UK, and currently lives in East London with his partner.

mattabbottpoet.com
@MattAbbottPoet